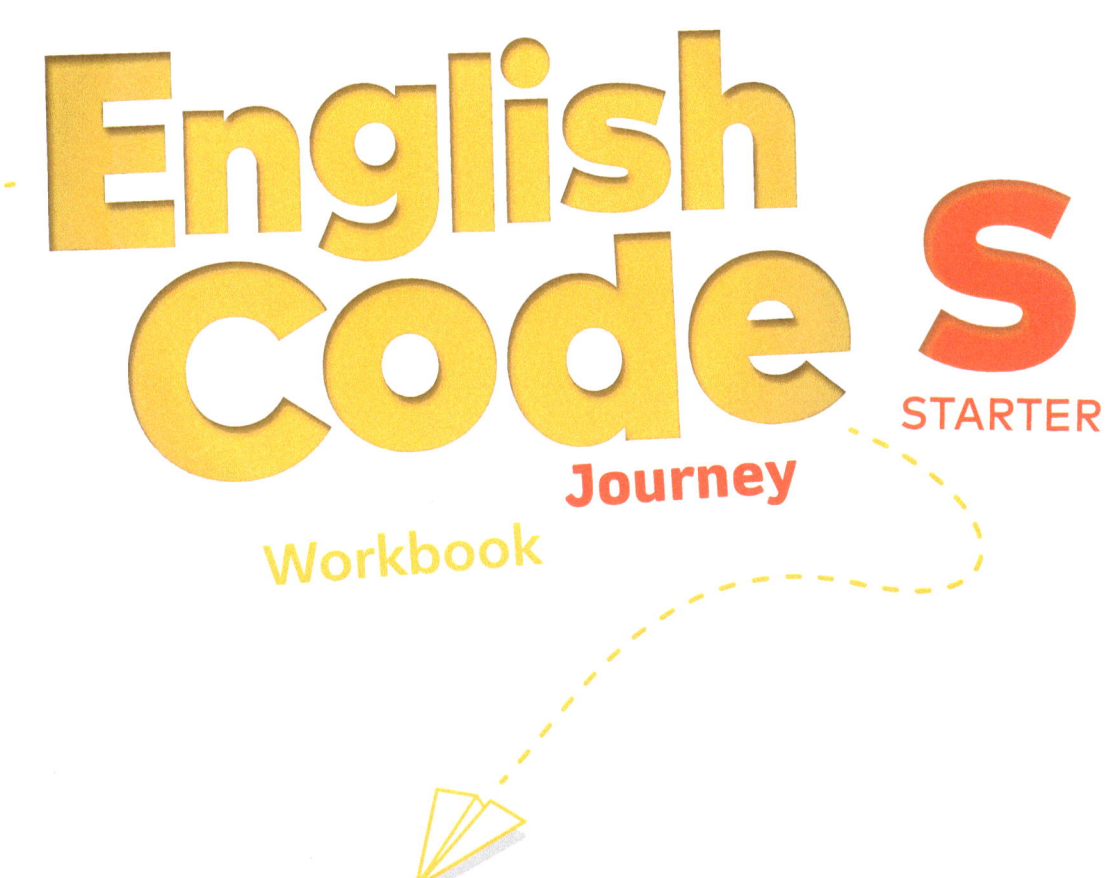

CONTENTS

WELCOME! .... P. 4

1 BIRTHDAY FUN! .... P. 6

2 MUSIC TIME! .... P. 16

3 AT THE FARM .... P. 26

CULTURE 1 .... P. 36

4 MY DINOSAUR .... P. 38

5 A PICNIC .... P. 48

6 UNDER THE SEA .... P. 58

CULTURE 2 .... P. 68

WELCOME!
HOW CAN I ENJOY MY FIRST DAY?

I WILL LEARN GREETINGS.

1 **LISTEN AND CHECK ☑. THEN SAY.**

1 **A**  **B**    2 **A**  **B**

3 **A**  **B**    4 **A**  **B**

2 **LISTEN AND SING. THEN NUMBER THE PICTURES IN ORDER.**

A  **B**  **C**  **D**

3 **LISTEN AND ANSWER. THEN ASK AND ANSWER WITH A PARTNER.**

4

4 LOOK, COUNT, AND COLOR. THEN DRAW THE MISSING DOTS.

CODE CRACKER

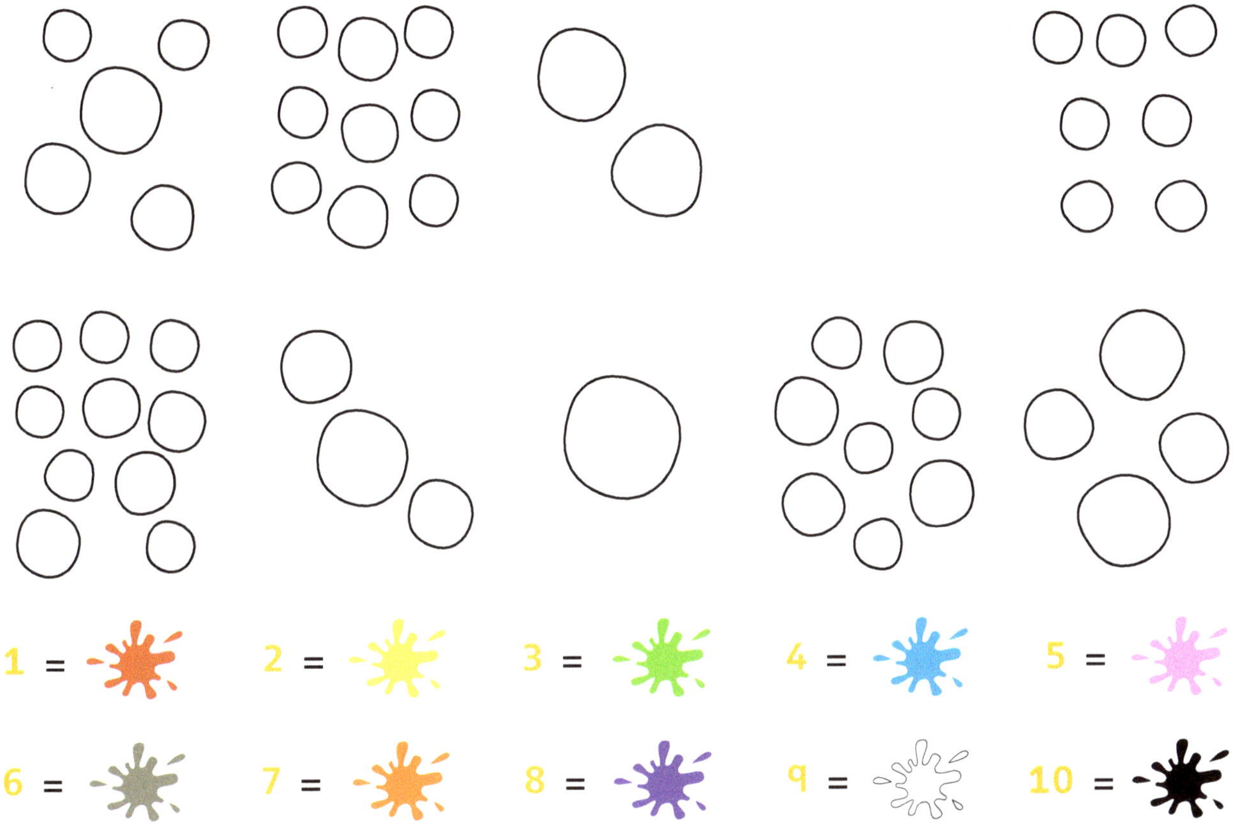

1 = 🟠   2 = 🟡   3 = 🟢   4 = 🔵   5 = 🩷
6 = ⚫   7 = 🟠   8 = 🟣   9 = ⚪   10 = ⚫

5 LISTEN AND NUMBER IN ORDER.

6 MAKE YOUR OWN NAME TAG. THEN SAY.

I CAN USE GREETINGS.

1 BIRTHDAY FUN!

HOW CAN I MAKE A BIRTHDAY CARD?

I WILL LEARN COLORS AND BIRTHDAY WORDS.

1. LISTEN AND CHECK ✓.

2. LISTEN AND SING. NUMBER IN ORDER.

3 LOOK. WHICH ITEMS DO NOT HAVE A PAIR? CIRCLE.

CODE CRACKER

4 LOOK AND SAY. TRACE.

MY PICTURE DICTIONARY!

BLUE CARD BALLOON CAKE

EXTRA VOCABULARY

5 LISTEN, POINT, AND SAY.

I CAN USE COLORS AND BIRTHDAY WORDS.

STORY LAB

ENJOYING A STORY

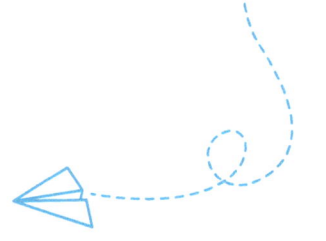
I WILL LISTEN TO A STORY ABOUT A BIRTHDAY.

HELLO FLUFFY!

1 REMEMBER THE STORY. NUMBER IN ORDER.

2 LISTEN AND CHECK YOUR ANSWERS.

3 LOOK AND CIRCLE THE CAKE FROM THE STORY.

CODE CRACKER

4 WHAT DO YOU THINK HAPPENS NEXT IN THE STORY? DRAW.

VALUES   TAKE CARE OF PETS.

5 CHECK ✓ OR CROSS ✗.

I CAN   LISTEN TO A STORY ABOUT A BIRTHDAY.

SOUND LAB
C AND B

I WILL LEARN THE C AND B SOUNDS.

1 COLOR AND MATCH. THEN LISTEN, POINT, AND SAY.

2 COLOR AND SAY.

3 LISTEN AND SAY.

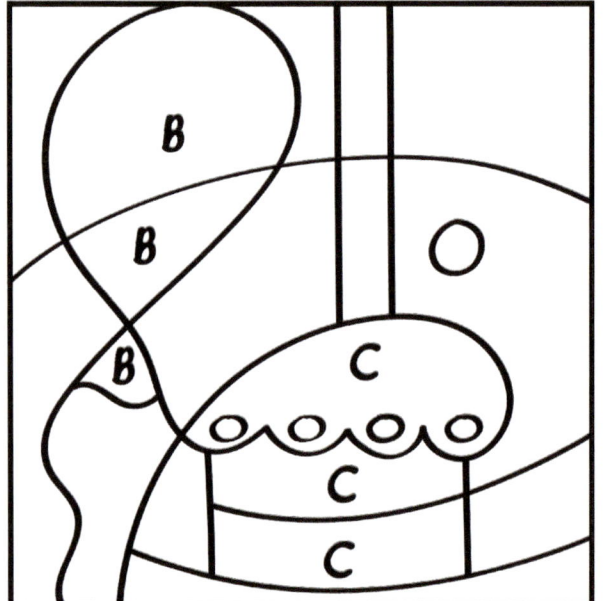

C =    B =

I CAN USE THE C AND B SOUNDS.

EXPERIMENT LAB

SCIENCE: RAINBOWS

I WILL LEARN ABOUT RAINBOWS.

1 COLOR THE RAINBOW. THEN SAY.

2 LOOK AND MATCH. THEN LISTEN AND POINT.

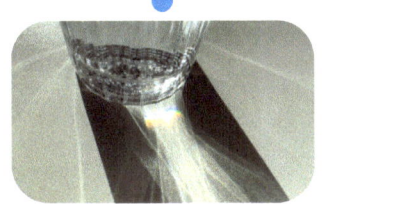      

3 MAKE A RAINBOW SPINNER.

I KNOW ABOUT RAINBOWS.

WHAT'S YOUR FAVORITE COLOR?

COMMUNICATION

I WILL ASK AND ANSWER ABOUT FAVORITE COLORS.

1 013 LISTEN AND CIRCLE *A* OR *B*. THEN SAY.

2 WHAT NUMBER ARE THE COLORS? WRITE.

3 COLOR WITH YOUR FAVORITE COLORS. PLAY *BINGO!*

MATH ZONE

$5 + \bullet = 6$

$4 + \bullet = 7$

$6 + \bullet = 8$

$\bullet = \underline{}$ $\bullet = \underline{}$

$\bullet = \underline{}$

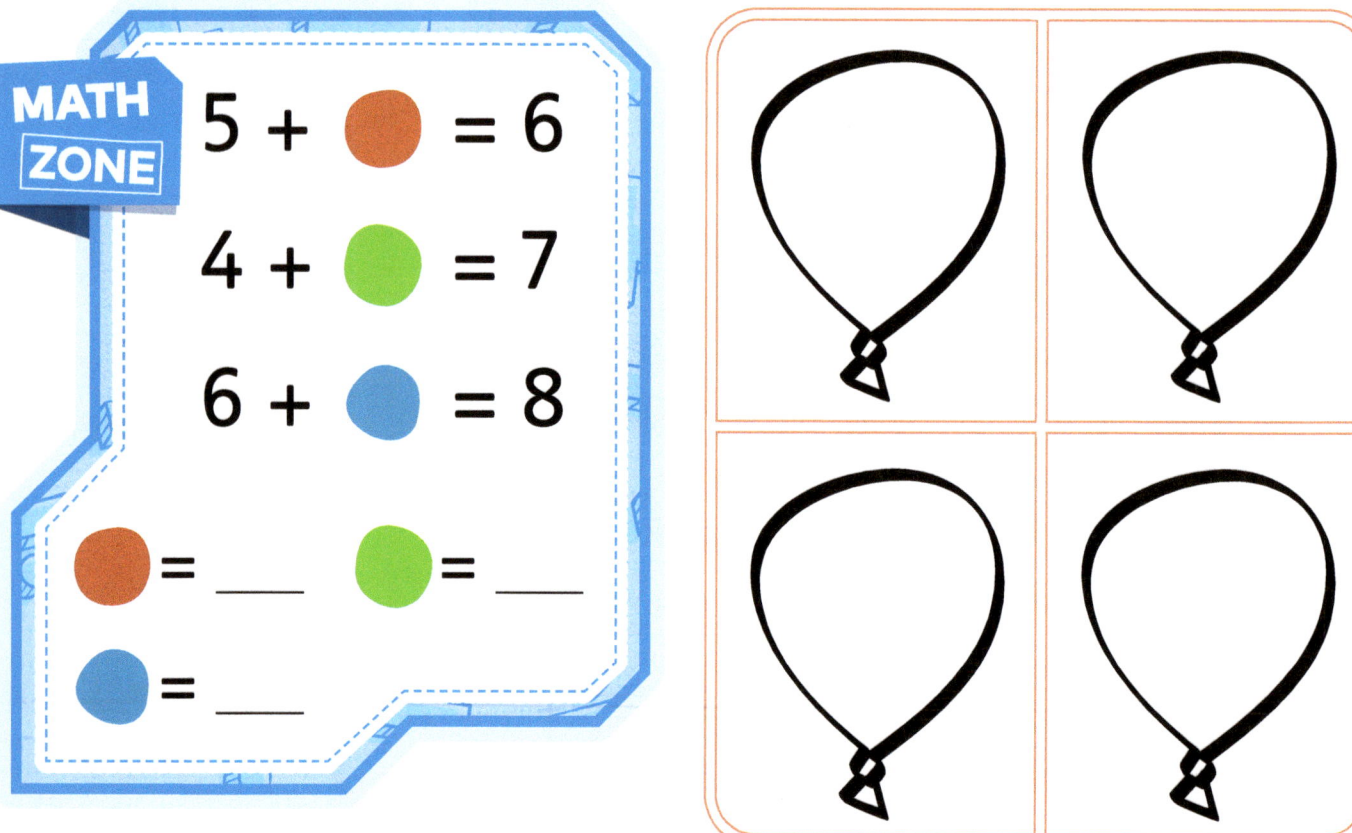

4 LISTEN AND NUMBER.

5 COLOR FOR YOU. THEN SAY.

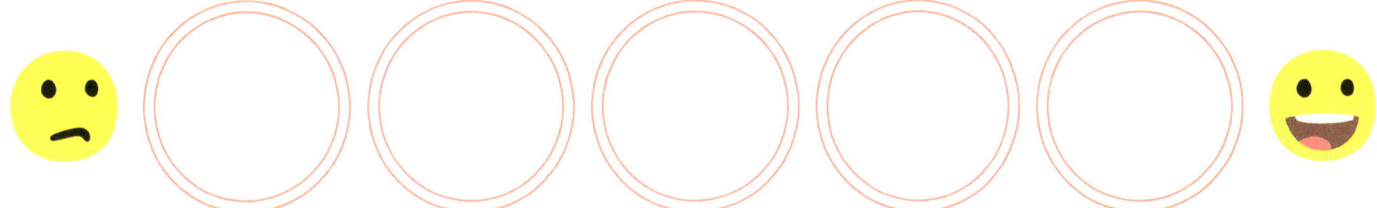

6 COLOR THE CORRECT NUMBER OF CANDLES FOR EACH COLOR. THEN SAY.

1X 🟢
2X 🟡
3X 🟠
4X 🔵

I CAN ASK AND ANSWER ABOUT FAVORITE COLORS.

PROJECT AND REVIEW UNIT 1

MAKE A BIRTHDAY CARD

PROJECT REPORT

1 WHAT COLORS DO YOU HAVE ON YOUR CARD? CHECK ✓.

2 LISTEN AND POINT. THEN COMPLETE YOUR PROJECT REPORT AND DRAW.

3 SHOW YOUR CARD TO YOUR FAMILY AND FRIENDS.

MY BIRTHDAY CARD FOR _____

I CAN MAKE A BIRTHDAY CARD.

REVIEW

1 🎧 LISTEN AND DRAW THE CANDLES.

2 🎨 DRAW AND COLOR FOR YOU. THEN SAY.

ALL ABOUT ME!

▶▶▶ NOW GO TO YOUR PROGRESS CHART ON PAGE 2.

2 MUSIC TIME!

HOW CAN I MAKE A MUSICAL INSTRUMENT?

I WILL LEARN MUSICAL INSTRUMENT WORDS.

1 🎧 017 **LISTEN AND CHECK ☑. THEN POINT AND SAY.**

2 🎧 018 **LISTEN AND SING. NUMBER IN ORDER.**

3 HELP LUCY GET TO THE PARTY. LISTEN AND FOLLOW THE PATH.

CODE CRACKER

4 LOOK AND SAY. THEN TRACE.

MY PICTURE DICTIONARY!

TRUMPET   DRUM   SING   PIANO

EXTRA VOCABULARY

5 LISTEN, POINT, AND SAY.

I CAN   USE MUSICAL INSTRUMENT WORDS.

STORY LAB

ENJOYING A STORY

I WILL LISTEN TO A STORY ABOUT MUSIC.

PLAY THE DRUM, FLUFFY!

1 REMEMBER THE STORY. NUMBER IN ORDER.

2 🎧 021 LISTEN AND CHECK YOUR ANSWERS.

3 🎧 022 LISTEN AND POINT TO THE PICTURES. WHICH ONES ARE NOT MUSIC? SAY.

4 LOOK AND MATCH. THEN LISTEN AND CHECK.

5 WHAT DO THEY PLAY? LISTEN AND CIRCLE.

6 WHAT DO YOU WANT TO PLAY? DRAW AND SAY.

 LISTEN TO A STORY ABOUT MUSIC.

SOUND LAB
T AND D

I WILL LEARN THE **T** AND **D** SOUNDS.

1 🎧 025 COLOR AND MATCH. THEN LISTEN, POINT, AND SAY.

2 💡 WHAT COMES NEXT? LOOK, CHECK ✓, AND SAY.

3 🎧 026 LISTEN AND FOLLOW. THEN SAY.

CODE CRACKER ⚙️

1      ?

? =  ☐    ☐

2   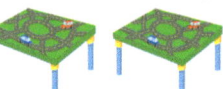  ?

? =  ☐    ☐

I CAN USE THE **T** AND **D** SOUNDS.

EXPERIMENT LAB
SCIENCE: SOUND WAVES

> I WILL LEARN ABOUT SOUND WAVES.

1  LISTEN AND POINT.

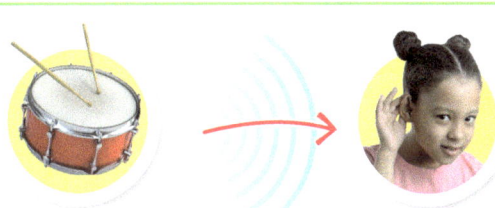

2 LOOK AND SAY. THEN MATCH.

3 DRAW AND COLOR THE WATER.

4 LOOK AND LISTEN. THEN USE TWO GLASSES AND A PENCIL TO COPY THE SOUNDS.

I KNOW ABOUT SOUND WAVES.

IT'S NOISY!

COMMUNICATION

I WILL TALK ABOUT MUSICAL SOUNDS.

1 LISTEN AND CIRCLE. THEN SAY.

2 LOOK, SORT, AND DRAW LINES. THEN SAY.

3 DRAW TWO QUIET THINGS AND TWO NOISY THINGS.

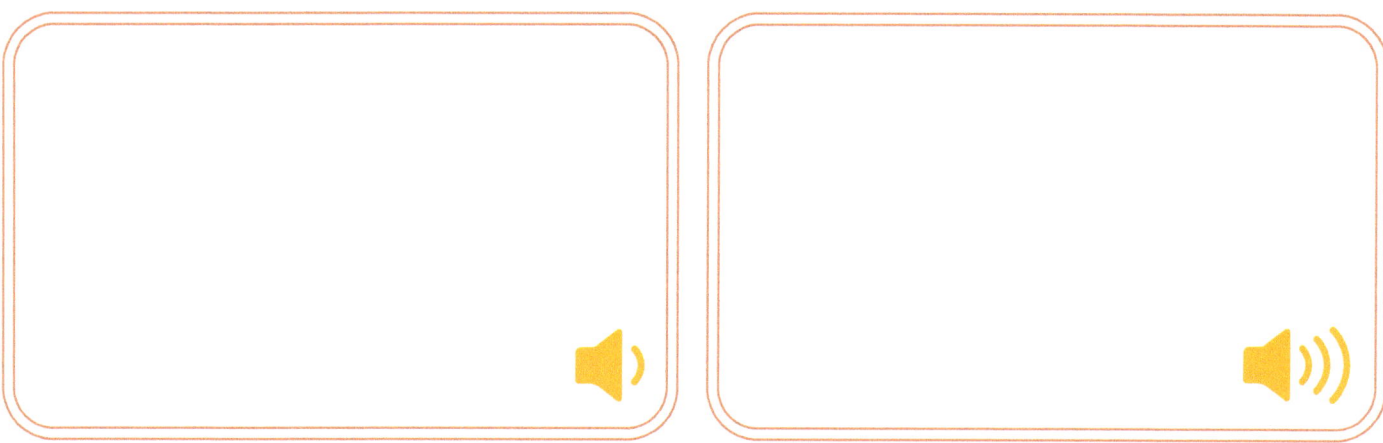

4 LOOK, COUNT, AND WRITE.

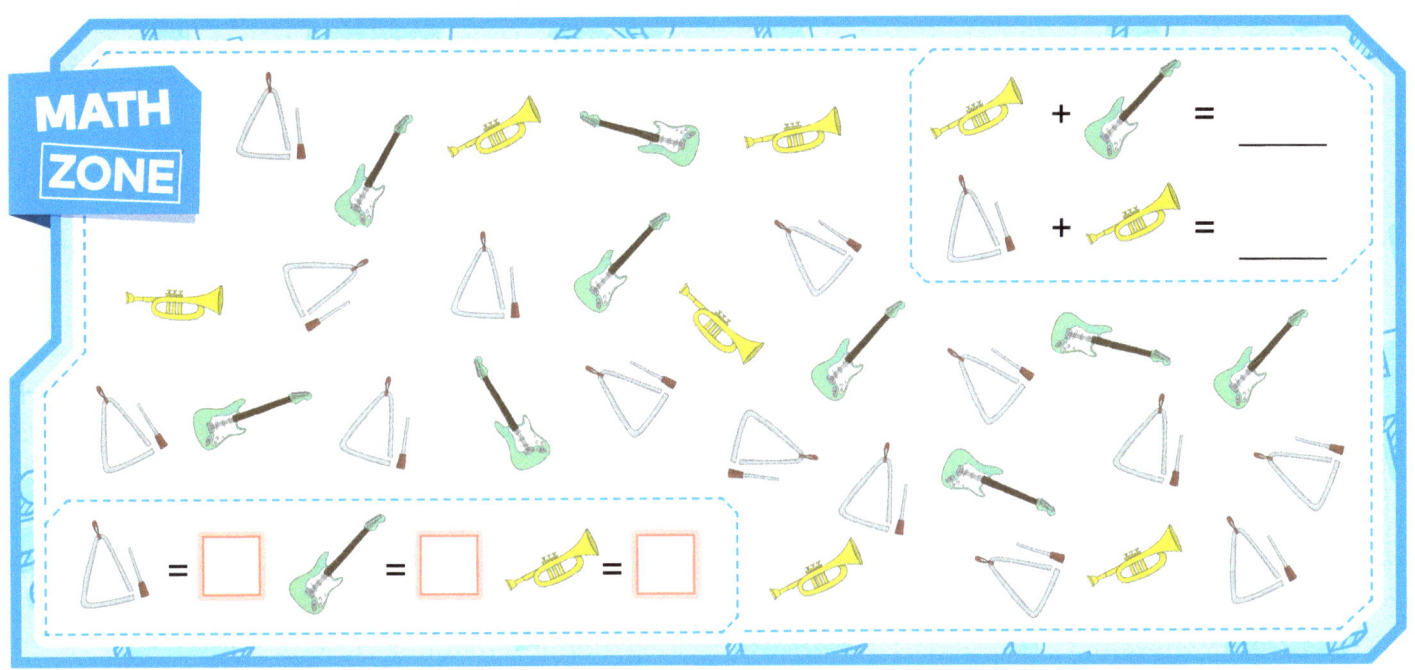

5 LISTEN. THEN PLAY THE GAME.

VALUES LISTEN TO EACH OTHER.

6 DO YOU LISTEN TO YOUR TEACHER AND YOUR FRIENDS? COLOR.

I CAN TALK ABOUT MUSICAL SOUNDS.

PROJECT AND REVIEW UNIT 2

MAKE A MUSICAL INSTRUMENT

1 WHAT DO YOU HAVE ON YOUR TABLE? CHECK ✓ AND SAY.

2 LISTEN AND POINT. THEN COMPLETE YOUR PROJECT REPORT AND DRAW.

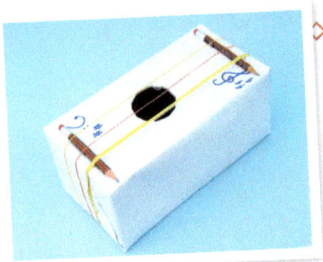

MY MUSICAL INSTRUMENT IS A _____ .

3 SHOW YOUR INSTRUMENT TO YOUR FAMILY AND FRIENDS.

I CAN MAKE A MUSICAL INSTRUMENT.

REVIEW

1 LISTEN AND NUMBER.

2 DRAW YOU AND YOUR FAVORITE INSTRUMENT. THEN SAY.

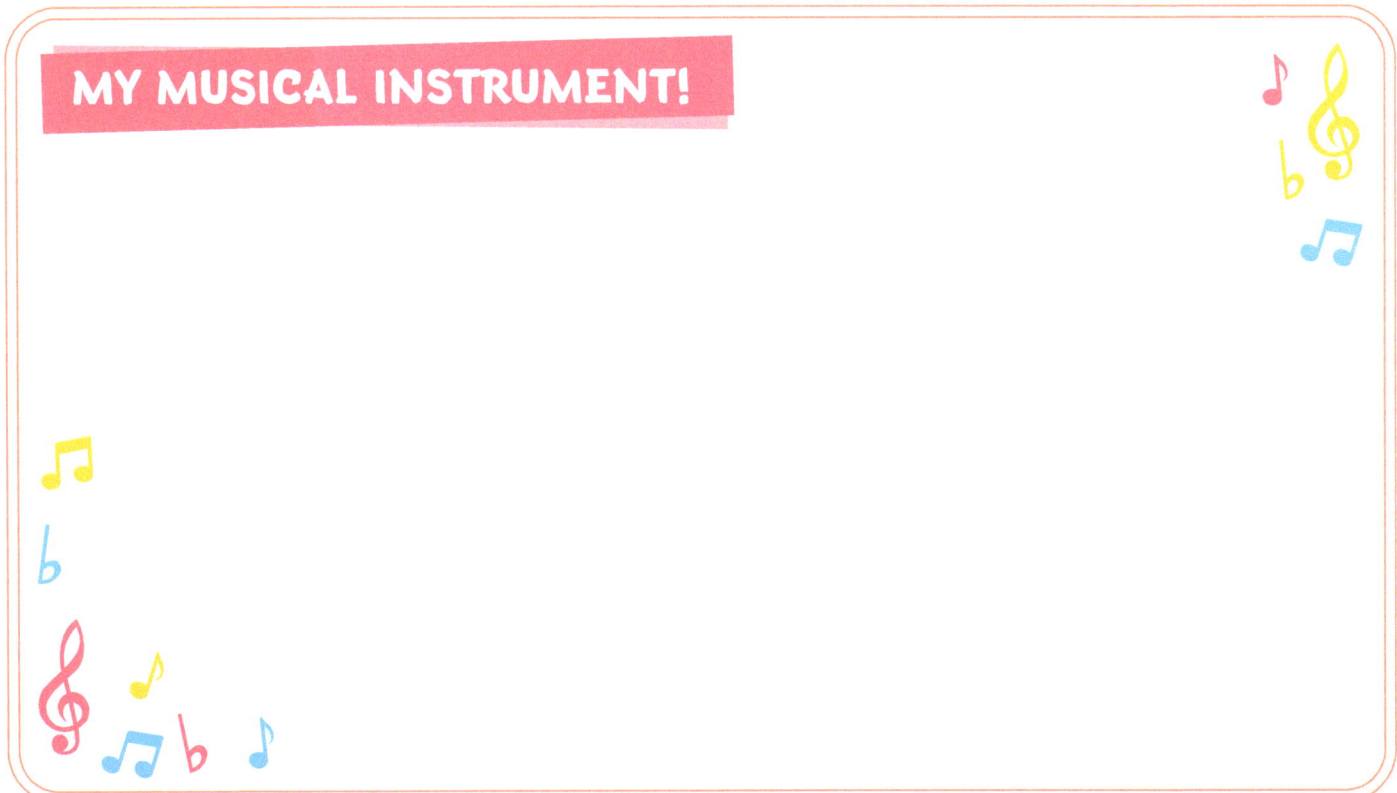

MY MUSICAL INSTRUMENT!

NOW GO TO YOUR PROGRESS CHART ON PAGE 2.

3 AT THE FARM

HOW CAN I MAKE A TOY FARM?

I WILL LEARN FARM WORDS.

1 FOLLOW AND CHECK ✓. THEN SAY.

2 LISTEN AND SING. NUMBER IN ORDER. WHAT'S MISSING?

3 CONTINUE THE SEQUENCE. THEN SAY.

CODE CRACKER

4 LOOK AND SAY. TRACE.

MY PICTURE DICTIONARY!

FOX   SHEEP   COW   TRACTOR

EXTRA VOCABULARY

5 LISTEN, POINT, AND SAY.

I CAN   USE FARM WORDS.

STORY LAB

ENJOYING A STORY

I WILL LISTEN TO A STORY ABOUT A FOX.

THE RED FOX

1 REMEMBER THE STORY. WHAT'S MISSING? NUMBER, THEN DRAW.

2 LISTEN AND CHECK YOUR ANSWERS.

3 WHAT DO THEY EAT IN THE STORY? MATCH AND SAY.

4 🎧 LISTEN AND CHECK ☑. THEN SAY.

5 COUNT AND DRAW. THEN SAY.

I CAN LISTEN TO A STORY ABOUT A FOX.

SOUND LAB
A AND F

I WILL LEARN THE A AND F SOUNDS.

1 COLOR AND MATCH. THEN LISTEN, POINT, AND SAY.

   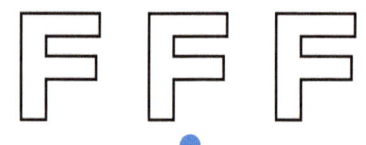

      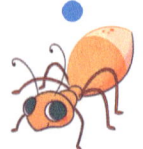   

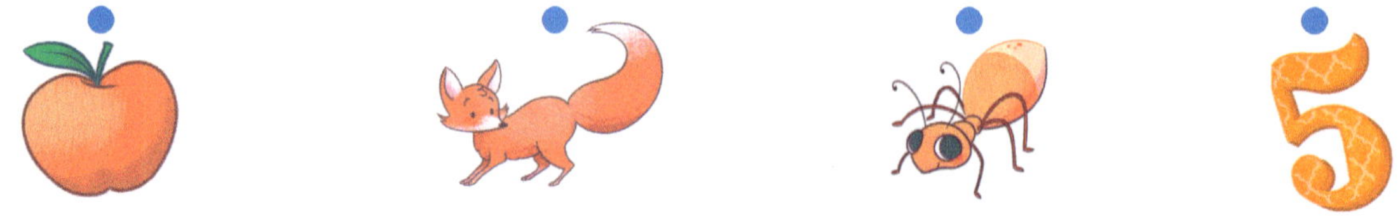

2 LISTEN AND CHECK ✓. THEN SAY.

3 SAY A TONGUE TWISTER FOR PICTURE 1.

4 FIND THE PATH. THEN COLOR AND SAY.

CODE CRACKER

A → P → C → F

I CAN USE THE A AND F SOUNDS.

EXPERIMENT LAB

SCIENCE: FOOD FROM ANIMALS

I WILL LEARN ABOUT FOOD FROM ANIMALS.

1 MATCH AND SAY. THEN LISTEN AND CHECK.

2 THINK AND DRAW.

3 THINK ABOUT YOUR EXPERIMENT. THEN NUMBER IN ORDER.

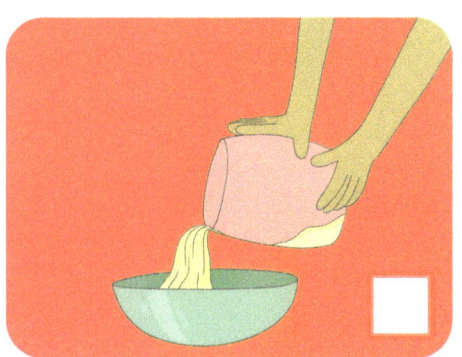

I KNOW ABOUT FOOD FROM ANIMALS.

SHUT THE GATE!

COMMUNICATION

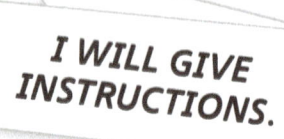

1 LISTEN AND CHECK ☑.

2 LISTEN AND CHECK ☑ THE CORRECT SEQUENCE.

3 🗨 LOOK AND SAY A SEQUENCE FROM 2.

4 ▶ NUMBER IN ORDER. WATCH THE VIDEO AGAIN TO CHECK.

5 🎨 MAKE A GATE. ROLE-PLAY THE VIDEO WITH A PARTNER.

VALUES TAKE CARE OF ANIMALS.

6 LOOK AND CIRCLE 😀 OR ☹.

😀 ☹   😀 ☹

I CAN GIVE INSTRUCTIONS.

33

PROJECT AND REVIEW UNIT 3

MAKE A TOY FARM

PROJECT REPORT

1 WHAT DO YOU HAVE ON YOUR FARM? WRITE THE NUMBER.

2 LISTEN AND POINT. THEN COMPLETE YOUR PROJECT REPORT AND DRAW.

THIS IS MY _____.

3 SHOW YOUR DRAWING IN 2 TO YOUR FAMILY AND FRIENDS.

I CAN MAKE A TOY FARM.

REVIEW

1 LISTEN AND WRITE THE NUMBERS.

2 DRAW AND COLOR FOR YOU. THEN SAY.

NOW GO TO YOUR PROGRESS CHART ON PAGE 2.

CULTURE 1
ANIMALS IN MUSIC

1 🎧 044 **LISTEN AND NUMBER. THEN ROLE-PLAY.**

2 🎧 045 **WHAT ANIMALS ARE IN THE SONGS? LISTEN AND CHECK ☑.**

1 A  B    2 A  B

3 A  B    4 A  B

3 **WHAT SONGS DO YOU KNOW ABOUT ANIMALS? TELL A PARTNER.**

4 PLAY YOUR MUSICAL INSTRUMENT. TELL AND SHARE.

4 MY DINOSAUR

HOW CAN I MAKE A DINOSAUR PUZZLE?

I WILL LEARN DINOSAUR WORDS.

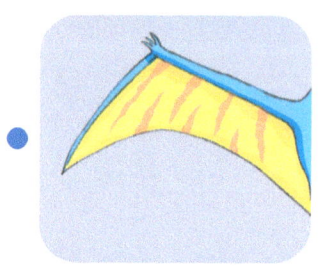

1 WHAT DO THEY HAVE? MATCH AND SAY.

2 🎵 046 LISTEN AND SING. NUMBER IN ORDER. DRAW ANOTHER ACTION FROM THE SONG.

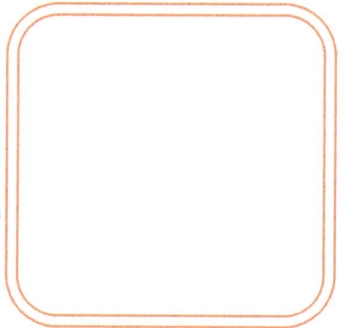

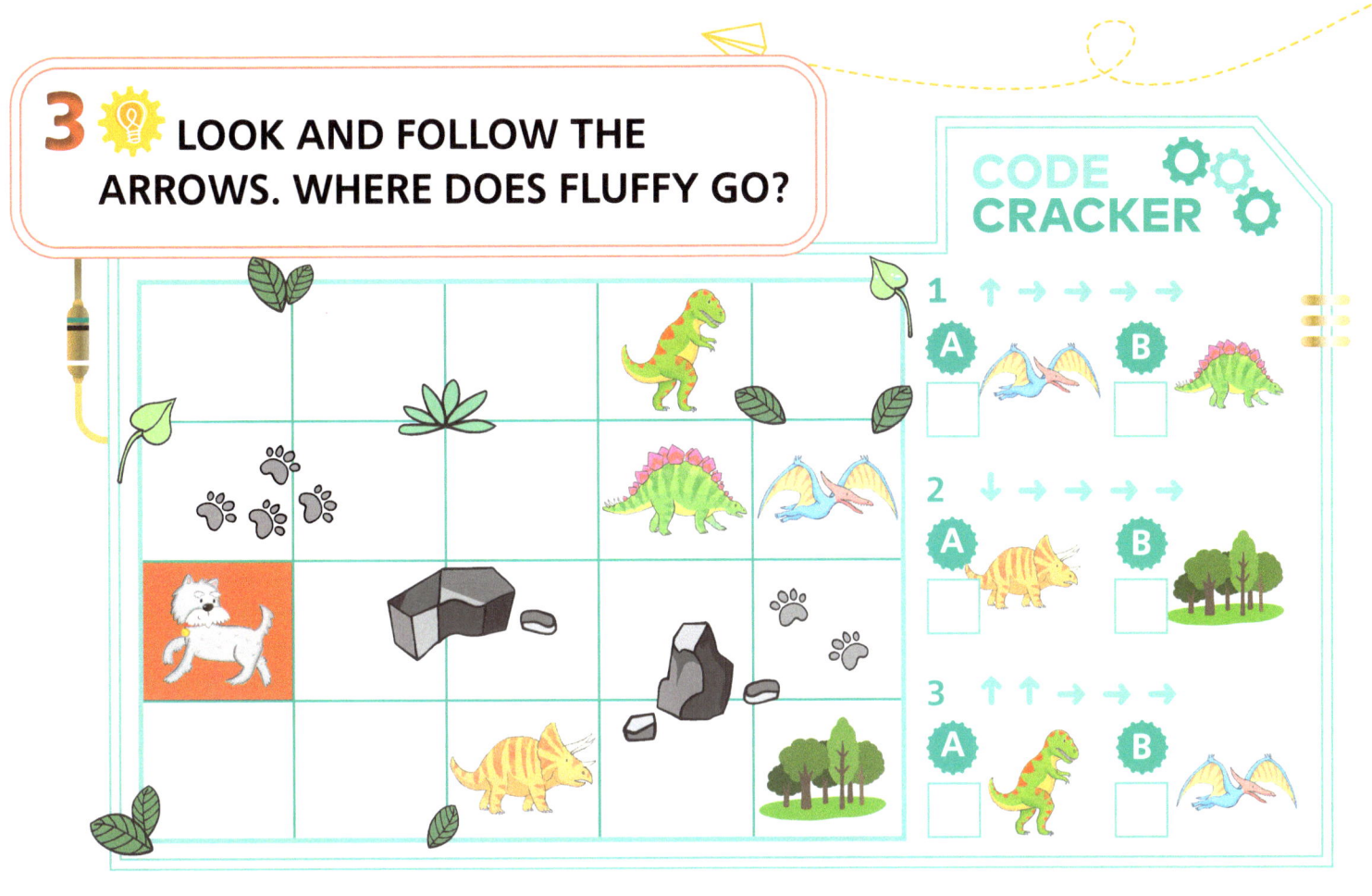

3 LOOK AND FOLLOW THE ARROWS. WHERE DOES FLUFFY GO?

CODE CRACKER

1 ↑ → → → →
   A B

2 ↓ → → → →
   A B

3 ↑ ↑ → → →
   A B

4 LOOK AND SAY. TRACE.

MY PICTURE DICTIONARY!

LIZARD   TAIL   LEGS   SPIKES

EXTRA VOCABULARY

5 LISTEN, POINT, AND SAY. THEN SING AND DO THE ACTIONS.

1   2   3   4

I CAN USE DINOSAUR WORDS.

STORY LAB

ENJOYING A STORY

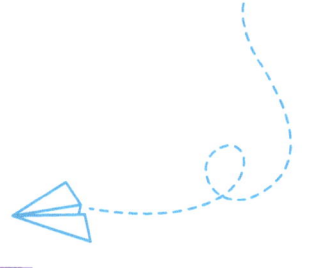

I WILL LISTEN TO A STORY ABOUT A DINOSAUR.

IT'S A DINOSAUR!

1 REMEMBER THE STORY. NUMBER IN ORDER.

2 LISTEN AND CHECK YOUR ANSWERS.

3 LISTEN AND CIRCLE.

1 A / B   2 A / B
3 A / B   4 A / B
5 A / B   6 A / B

4 DRAW TWO ANIMALS. PLAY THE GAME FROM 3 WITH A PARTNER.

A

B

5 FIND FOUR DIFFERENCES. THEN SAY.

I CAN LISTEN TO A STORY ABOUT A DINOSAUR.

SOUND LAB
L AND E

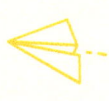

I WILL LEARN THE L AND E SOUNDS.

1 TRACE AND MATCH. THEN LISTEN, POINT, AND SAY.

LIZARD   ELEPHANT   LEGS   EGG

2 LOOK AND WRITE L OR E. THEN SAY.

1. L_UNCH
2. ____ ____GS
3. ____ ____BOW
4. ____ ____ ____PHANT

3 COLOR AND SAY.

L = 🟢   E = 🩷

I CAN USE THE L AND E SOUNDS.

42

EXPERIMENT LAB

SCIENCE: WHAT DINOSAURS EAT

I WILL LEARN ABOUT WHAT DINOSAURS EAT.

1 LISTEN. THEN LOOK AND MATCH.

2 LOOK, SORT, AND DRAW LINES.

3 DRAW MORE ANIMALS FOR EACH SECTION IN **2**.

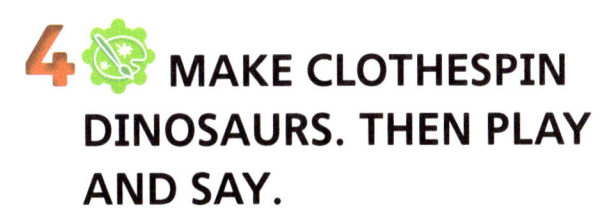

4 MAKE CLOTHESPIN DINOSAURS. THEN PLAY AND SAY.

I KNOW ABOUT WHAT DINOSAURS EAT.

43

IS IT A DINOSAUR?

COMMUNICATION

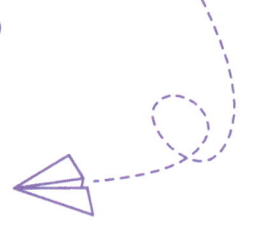

I WILL GIVE SUPPORT TO MY FRIENDS.

1 🎧 **LISTEN AND CHECK ☑.**

2 🎧 **LISTEN AND DRAW. THEN COMPARE WITH A PARTNER.**

3 💬 **THINK OF AN ANIMAL. DESCRIBE IT TO A PARTNER TO DRAW.**

IT HAS FOUR LEGS.

4 LOOK, COUNT, AND WRITE.

MATH ZONE

☐ × ☐ = ☐

☐ × ☐ = ☐

5 WHAT'S IN THE BAG? LISTEN AND CIRCLE.

6 PLAY *FEELY BAG*. SAY *GOOD JOB!* OR *NICE TRY!*

I CAN GIVE SUPPORT TO MY FRIENDS.

PROJECT AND REVIEW UNIT 4

MAKE A DINOSAUR PUZZLE

PROJECT REPORT

1 WHAT DOES YOUR DINOSAUR HAVE? CHECK ✓.

1 2 3 4 5

2 COMPLETE YOUR PROJECT REPORT. THEN DRAW.

MY DINOSAUR HAS

_____

_____ .

3 DO YOUR PUZZLE WITH FAMILY AND FRIENDS.

I CAN MAKE A DINOSAUR PUZZLE.

REVIEW

1 CIRCLE THE ODD ONE OUT. THEN SAY.

2 DRAW YOUR FAVORITE DINOSAUR. THEN SAY.

MY FAVORITE DINOSAUR!

NOW GO TO YOUR PROGRESS CHART ON PAGE 2.

5 A PICNIC

▷ HOW CAN WE HAVE A PICNIC?

I WILL LEARN PICNIC WORDS.

1 🎧 055 LISTEN AND CHECK ☑. THEN SAY.

1 A B
2 A B
3 A B
4 A B

2 🎧 056 LISTEN AND SING. LISTEN TO VERSE 1 AND CHECK ☑ THE PICNIC.

1

2

3 LISTEN AND NUMBER.

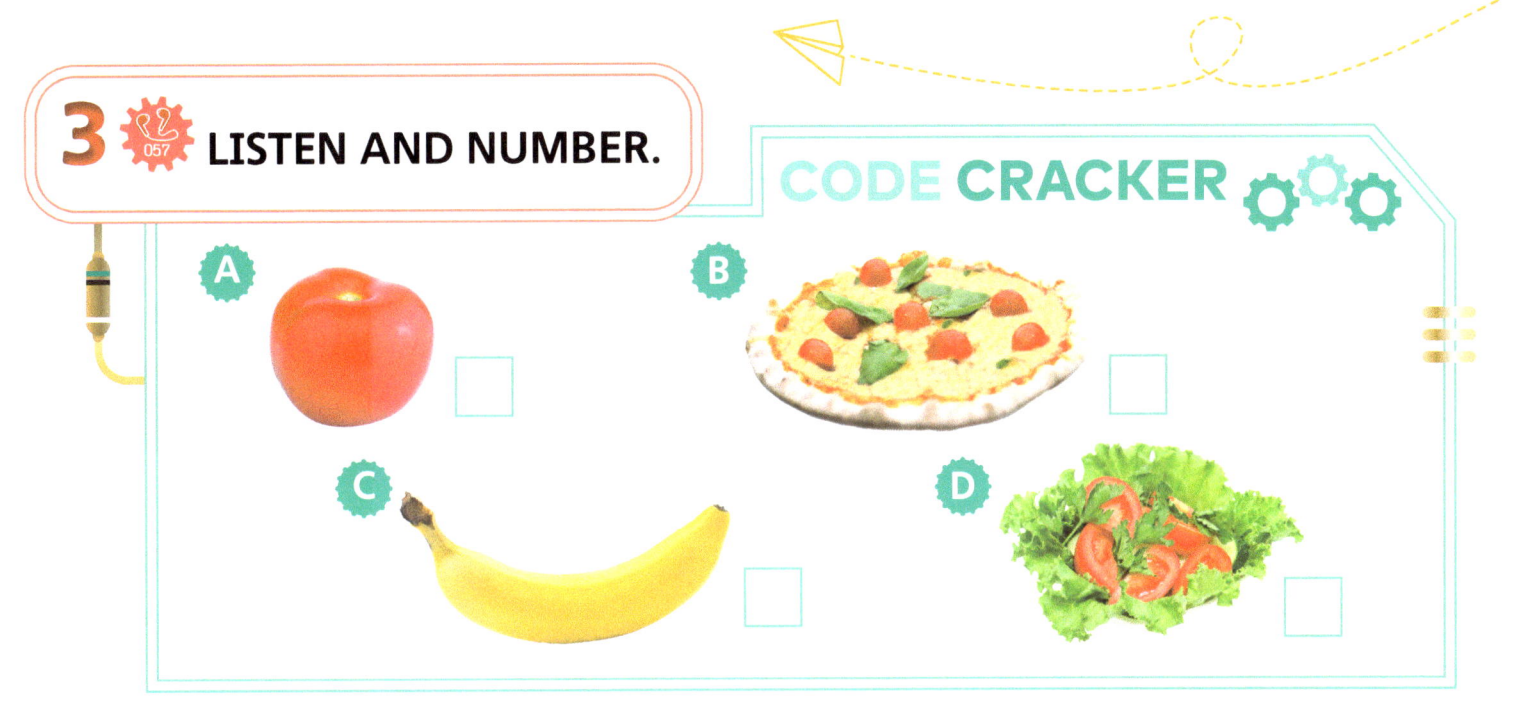

CODE CRACKER

A
B
C
D

4 LOOK AND SAY. TRACE.

MY PICTURE DICTIONARY!

YOGURT   PIZZA   FRUIT   SALAD

EXTRA VOCABULARY

5 LISTEN, POINT, AND SAY.

1
2
3
4

I CAN   USE PICNIC WORDS.

STORY LAB

ENJOYING A STORY

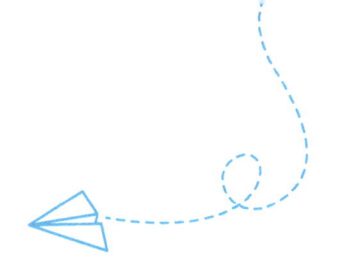

I WILL LISTEN TO A STORY ABOUT A PICNIC.

PICNIC TIME

1 REMEMBER THE STORY. WHAT'S MISSING? NUMBER, THEN DRAW.

2 LISTEN AND CHECK YOUR ANSWERS.

3 LOOK AND CHECK ☑ THE FOOD FROM THE STORY. THEN SAY.

1. 2. 3. 4. 5. 6.

4 LISTEN AND DRAW 😃 OR ☹. THEN SAY.

1 A B
2 A B
3 A B
4 A B

VALUES LEARN TO SHARE.

5 WHAT CAN YOU SHARE? CHECK ☑.

1. 2. 3. 4.

6 WHAT DO YOU LIKE AT A PICNIC? DRAW.

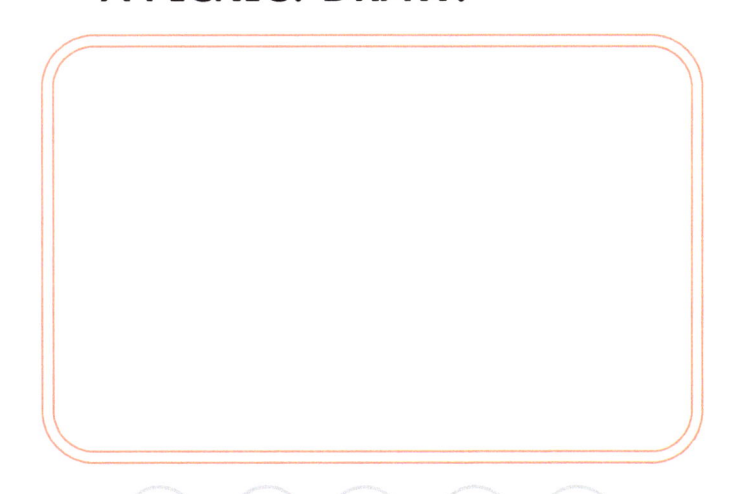

I CAN LISTEN TO A STORY ABOUT A PICNIC.

51

SOUND LAB
Y AND J

I WILL LEARN THE Y AND J SOUNDS.

1 🎧 061 TRACE AND MATCH. THEN LISTEN, POINT, AND SAY.

YO-YO   YELLOW   JUG   JAR

2 🎧 062 LISTEN AND CIRCLE Y OR J.

1. Y / J
2. Y / J
3. Y / J
4. Y / J

3 CIRCLE THE ODD ONE OUT.

1.
2.

I CAN USE THE Y AND J SOUNDS.

EXPERIMENT LAB

SCIENCE: QUANTITIES OF SUGAR

I WILL LEARN ABOUT SUGAR.

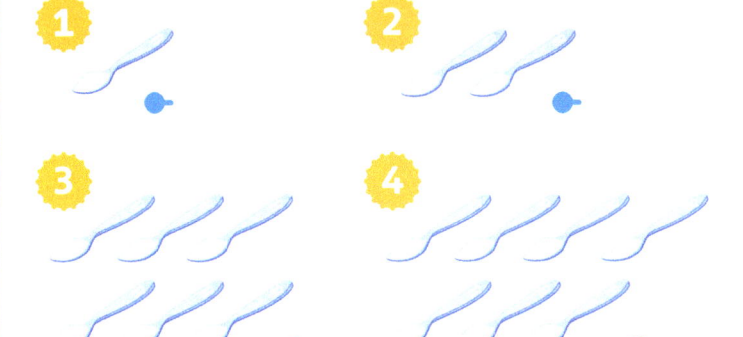

1 REMEMBER AND MATCH. THEN LISTEN AND CHECK.

2 LOOK AT THE ITEMS IN **1**. CALCULATE THE SUGAR.

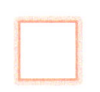

3 LOOK AND COMPLETE THE BAR CHART. USE YOUR EXPERIMENT TIME RESULTS.

I KNOW ABOUT SUGAR.

53

WASH YOUR HANDS!

COMMUNICATION

I WILL GIVE INSTRUCTIONS.

1 🎧 **LISTEN AND CHECK** ☑.

1 A   B
2 A   B
3 A   B
4 A   B

2 ▶ **SAY AND NUMBER IN ORDER. WATCH THE VIDEO AGAIN TO CHECK.**

VALUES WASH YOUR HANDS.

3 WHEN DO YOU WASH YOUR HANDS? CHECK ✓ AND SAY.

4 🎨 DECORATE A SOAP DISPENSER.

5 🎧 LISTEN, CHANT, AND ROLE-PLAY.

I CAN GIVE INSTRUCTIONS.

55

PROJECT AND REVIEW UNIT 5

HAVE A PICNIC

PROJECT REPORT

1 WHAT DO YOU HAVE IN YOUR PICNIC? CHECK ☑.

2 COMPLETE YOUR PROJECT REPORT. THEN DRAW.

IN MY PICNIC I HAVE
_____ .

3 🎧 066 LISTEN AND REPEAT. SHOW YOUR DRAWING IN 2 TO YOUR FAMILY AND FRIENDS.

I CAN HAVE A PICNIC.

REVIEW

1 🎧 067 LISTEN AND CHECK ☑ THE FOOD AT THE PICNIC.
THEN LISTEN AGAIN AND CIRCLE 😃 OR 😞.

1.
2.
3.
4.
5.
6.

2 DRAW AND COLOR FOR YOU. THEN SAY.

MY PICNIC!

▶▶▶ NOW GO TO YOUR PROGRESS CHART ON PAGE 2.

6 UNDER THE SEA

HOW CAN I MAKE A DIVING GAME?

I WILL LEARN SEA ANIMAL WORDS.

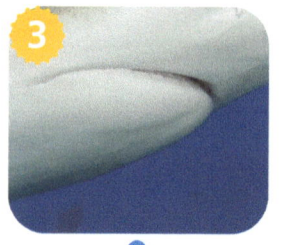

1 MATCH AND SAY.

2 WHAT'S MISSING FROM 1? DRAW AND SAY.

3 LISTEN AND SING. COLOR THE FISH IN ORDER.

4 WHICH ANIMALS ARE NOT A PAIR? CIRCLE.

CODE CRACKER

5 LOOK AND SAY. WRITE THE FIRST LETTER.

MY PICTURE DICTIONARY!

____RAB   ____HARK   ____HRIMP   ____ELLYFISH

EXTRA VOCABULARY

6 LISTEN, POINT, AND SAY.

1   2   3   4

I CAN USE SEA ANIMAL WORDS.

STORY LAB

ENJOYING A STORY

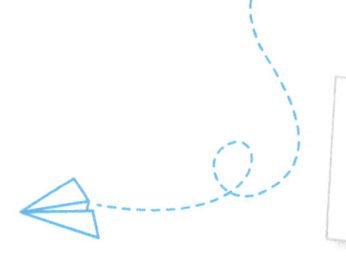

I WILL LISTEN TO A STORY ABOUT SEA ANIMALS.

CAN YOU SEE TEETH?

1 REMEMBER THE STORY. NUMBER IN ORDER.

2 LISTEN AND CHECK YOUR ANSWERS.

3 LISTEN AND CHECK ☑.

1

2

4 LISTEN AND DRAW.

5 DRAW A FISH TANK IN YOUR NOTEBOOK. ASK AND ANSWER WITH A PARTNER.

I CAN LISTEN TO A STORY ABOUT SEA ANIMALS.

SOUND LAB
I AND U

I WILL LEARN THE I AND U SOUNDS.

1 WRITE, TRACE, AND MATCH. THEN LISTEN, POINT, AND SAY.

__P   __NSECT   __MBRELLA   __GLOO

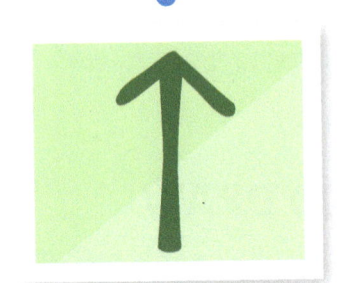

2 WHICH TWO MATCH? CIRCLE.

CODE CRACKER

3 LISTEN, POINT, AND SAY.

I CAN USE THE I AND U SOUNDS.

EXPERIMENT LAB

SCIENCE: ANIMALS WITH SHELLS

I WILL LEARN ABOUT ANIMALS WITH SHELLS.

1 CHECK ✓ THE ANIMALS WITH SHELLS.

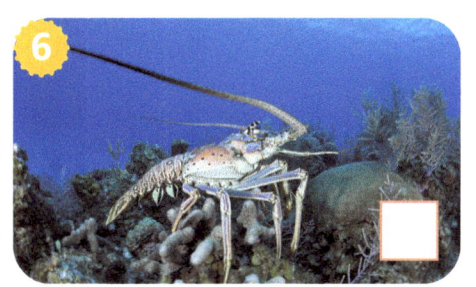

2 LOOK, SORT, AND DRAW LINES.

3 DRAW MORE ANIMALS FOR EACH SECTION IN **2**.

4 MAKE A SHELL CRAB.

I KNOW ABOUT ANIMALS WITH SHELLS.

IT'S WINDY!

COMMUNICATION

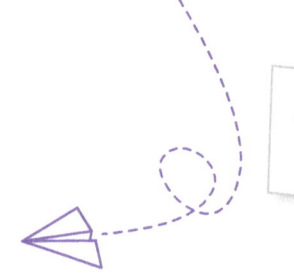

I WILL TALK ABOUT THE WEATHER.

1. LISTEN AND CHECK ☑.

2. CONTINUE THE SEQUENCE. THEN SAY.

CODE CRACKER

VALUES WEAR SUITABLE CLOTHES.

3 ARE THE CHILDREN WEARING THE CORRECT CLOTHES? LOOK AND CHECK ✓ OR CROSS ✗. THEN SAY.

4 MAKE DRESS-UP DOLLS.

5 PLAY WITH YOUR DOLLS AND SAY.

IT'S HOT!

I CAN TALK ABOUT THE WEATHER.

PROJECT AND REVIEW UNIT 6

MAKE A DIVING GAME

PROJECT REPORT

1 WHAT DOES YOUR DIVING GAME HAVE? CHECK ☑.

2 COMPLETE YOUR PROJECT REPORT. THEN DRAW.

MY DIVING TANK HAS _____ _____ .

3 LISTEN AND SAY. PLAY YOUR GAME WITH FRIENDS AND FAMILY.

I CAN MAKE A DIVING GAME.

REVIEW

1. LISTEN. WHAT'S ON THE TRAY? CHECK ✓ OR CROSS ✗.

1.
2.
3.
4.
5.

2. DRAW YOUR FAVORITE SEA ANIMALS. THEN SAY.

MY FAVORITE SEA ANIMALS!

NOW GO TO YOUR PROGRESS CHART ON PAGE 2.

CULTURE 2
LUNCH ON THE GO

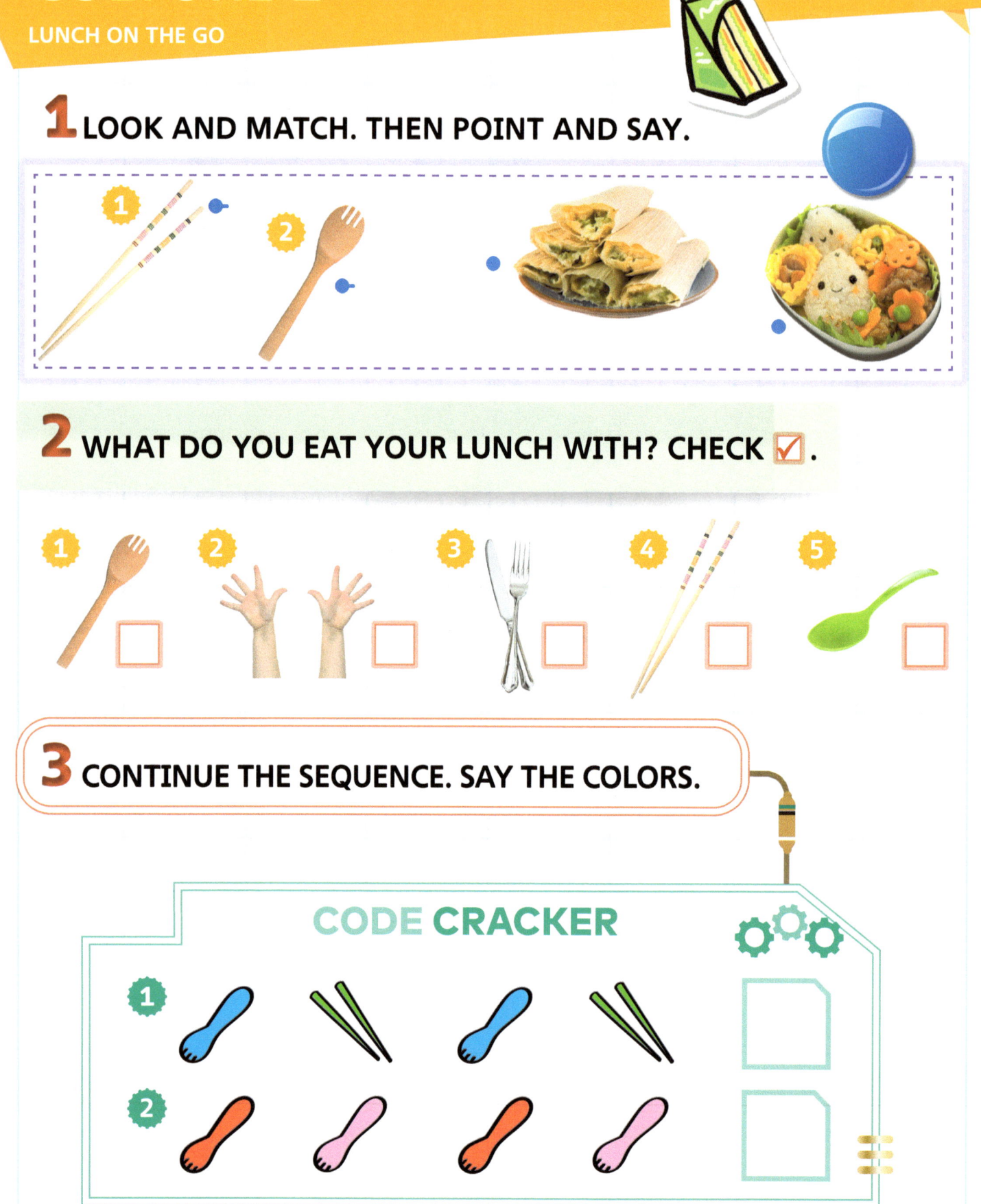

1 LOOK AND MATCH. THEN POINT AND SAY.

2 WHAT DO YOU EAT YOUR LUNCH WITH? CHECK ✓.

3 CONTINUE THE SEQUENCE. SAY THE COLORS.

CODE CRACKER

4 WHAT DO YOU HAVE IN YOUR LUNCHBOX? DRAW.

OUR WORLD

INTRO:
HERE WE STAND: CHILDREN OF EVERY AGE,
THIS IS OUR WORLD AND THE WORLD'S OUR STAGE.
WE CAN LAUGH, WE CAN CRY – WE CAN FLOAT, WE CAN FLY,
WE CAN DANCE, WE CAN SING – WE CAN DO ALMOST ANYTHING
IN *OUR* WORLD ... OUR *BEAUTIFUL* WORLD.

VERSE 1:
SOME OF US ARE SMALL; SOME OF US ARE TALL,
SOME OF US ARE SHY; SOME SAY HI TO EVERYBODY,
SOME OF US LIKE NUMBERS; SOME OF US LOVE WORDS,
SOME OF US WATCH FOOTBALL, AND SOME OF US WATCH THE BIRDS!

(CHORUS)
THIS IS OUR WORLD ... WE'RE DIFFERENT BUT THE SAME.
WE LIVE AND LEARN TOGETHER – WE GET TO KNOW EACH OTHER ...
IN *OUR* WORLD ... OUR *BEAUTIFUL* WORLD.

VERSE 2:
SOME OF US LIKE MUSIC; SOME OF US LIKE CARS,
SOME OF US DRAW PICTURES, LOOKING AT THE STARS,
SOME OF US ARE SCIENTISTS, TRYING TO FIND THE CODE,
ALL OF US CAN HELP A FRIEND AND GIVE A HAND TO HOLD.

THIS IS OUR WORLD – THERE'S ROOM FOR EVERYONE.
WE LEARN TO LIVE TOGETHER, AND WE HAVE A LOT OF FUN ...
IN *OUR* WORLD ... IN *OUR* WORLD ... IN OUR BEAUTIFUL WORLD!

Aa Bb Cc Dd Ee
Ff Gg Hh Ii Jj
Kk Ll Mm Nn Oo
Pp Qq Rr Ss Uu
Vv Ww Xx Yy Zz

PROGRESS CHART STICKERS

UNIT 1

CREATIVITY | CRITICAL THINKING | CODING | COMMUNICATION

UNIT 2

CREATIVITY | CRITICAL THINKING | CODING | COMMUNICATION

UNIT 3

CREATIVITY | CRITICAL THINKING | CODING | COMMUNICATION

PROGRESS CHART STICKERS

UNIT 4

CREATIVITY | CRITICAL THINKING | CODING | COMMUNICATION

UNIT 5

CREATIVITY | CRITICAL THINKING | CODING | COMMUNICATION

UNIT 6

CREATIVITY | CRITICAL THINKING | CODING | COMMUNICATION